60193

BUFO

THE STORY OF A TOAD

written and illustrated by

ROBERT M. McCLUNG

WILLIAM MORROW AND COMPANY
New York   1954

．　．　．　．　．　．　．　．　．

Green curled leaves of skunk
cabbage peeked out of the water.
Yellow cowslips were in bloom. It
was late May in the meadow pond.

3

A bullfrog's deep chug-a-rum sounded from the shallows, then the trill of a tree frog, then a whole chorus of toads.

When a male toad trilled, his throat swelled out like a balloon— bigger—and bigger—and bigger! A high trembling note came out, loud and clear; then it stopped abruptly. It was springtime—egg-laying time.

Lots of animals laid eggs in and around the pond. On the bank a snapping turtle was digging a hole to bury her eggs. On her nest among the reeds a red-winged blackbird sat on four spotted eggs.

A bullfrog was laying her masses of eggs in the shallow water by the bank. A male sunfish stood guard over the eggs in his sand nest on the pond bottom.

May flies were dropping their egg cases on the surface of the water, and a pond snail was laying her eggs on a lily pad. A newt had already laid her eggs there.

Eggs, eggs, eggs! And the fe-
male toads were laying eggs too.

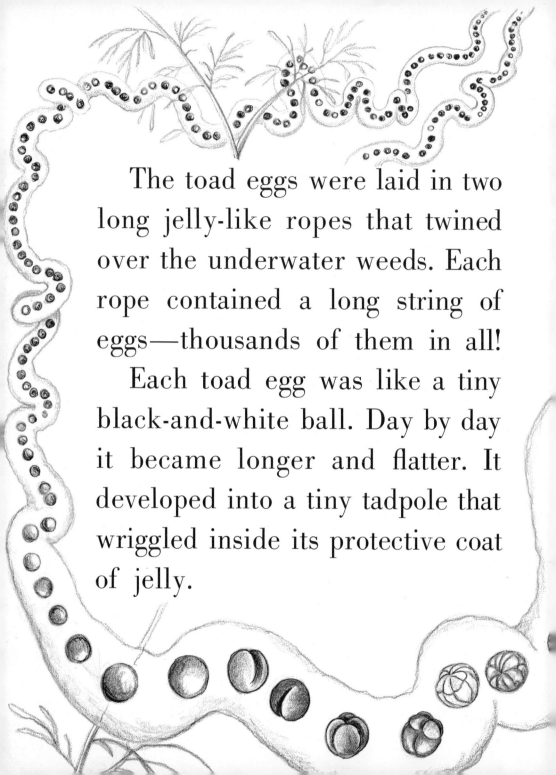

The toad eggs were laid in two long jelly-like ropes that twined over the underwater weeds. Each rope contained a long string of eggs—thousands of them in all!

Each toad egg was like a tiny black-and-white ball. Day by day it became longer and flatter. It developed into a tiny tadpole that wriggled inside its protective coat of jelly.

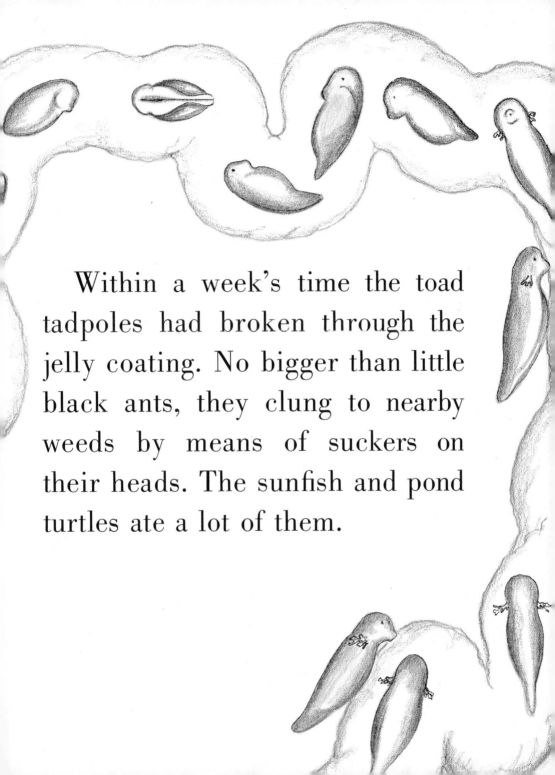

Within a week's time the toad
tadpoles had broken through the
jelly coating. No bigger than little
black ants, they clung to nearby
weeds by means of suckers on
their heads. The sunfish and pond
turtles ate a lot of them.

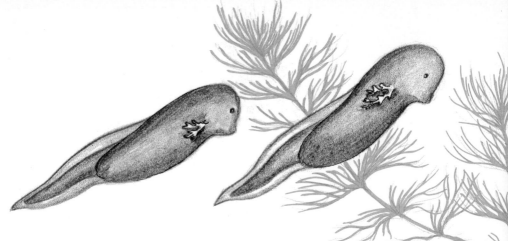

After several days the little tadpoles began to swim, wiggling their tails vigorously. It was almost ten days after they had hatched before their mouths developed and they could eat. They had tiny oval mouths, lined with rows of horny bumps, like teeth. The tadpoles ate algae and other tiny plants, which they scraped from the rocks.

Each tadpole breathed the oxygen in the water by means of tiny gills that branched out like feathers on either side of its head. After a few days a thin layer of skin grew back over the gills and hid them from sight.

Lots of animals found the little toad tadpoles good to eat. A dragonfly nymph caught one in its hinged jaws and ate it. A giant water beetle ate several more. A duckling gobbled up others. But some of the toad tadpoles escaped and lived and grew.

Bufo was one of these. He almost got eaten when a catfish chased him, but he escaped by swimming into the reeds and hiding under a leaf. He stayed among the reeds, eating and growing and changing.

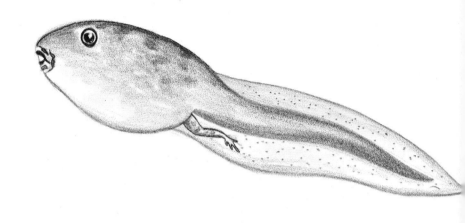

Tiny buds grew out from his body on each side of his tail. These quickly grew into little hind legs with webbed toes. By the middle of July, Bufo was an inch long. He was black, spotted with flecks of gold.

Bufo's front legs had been growing too, underneath the skin. Finally his left front leg came popping out through the breathing pore on that side. His right front leg broke through the skin on the other side.

The tadpole was fast becoming a little toad. Bufo's round head became flatter and his eyes grew larger. His small oval mouth became wide and gaping. He still had his long tail, though.

But the tail began to get shorter and shorter. Soon it had disappeared entirely!

Bufo breathed air now. His tadpole gills had disappeared, and lungs had developed to take their place.

Bufo had changed from a tadpole into a tiny toad, less than half an inch long. The change had been strange and wonderful.

Now it was time for him to leave the pond. One day, after a rain, Bufo and many of the other little toads hopped out of the water. They set out across the meadow, looking for tiny insects to eat.

But other animals were looking for tiny toads to eat. A garter snake ate several of them. A starling ate some more. But Bufo escaped!

On and on he hopped, through
the low meadow.

Into the farmyard.

Through the pigpen.

Past the big garden.

Hop—hop—hop!

Finally he reached the spring-house. Beside the cool spring was a big mossy rock. Under the rock was a snug little cave. Bufo hopped in and there he stayed.

All summer long the cool damp hole under the rock was his resting place by day, and the big garden was his hunting ground each night. Bufo's appetite was enormous. Every night he ate all the insects he could find. He grew bigger and fatter. By autumn he was over an inch long.

When cold weather came and there were no more insects to eat, Bufo backed himself farther into his hole, digging with his hind feet. The loosened earth fell in on top of him. All winter long he stayed in his hole, snug and asleep.

Late one afternoon the next spring, Bufo woke up. He forced his way through the earth and hopped out from under the rock.

Above him was a gnarled old apple tree. A butterfly was drinking nectar from the apple blossoms. A pair of robins, recently returned from their winter home in the South, were building a nest in a forked branch.

Bufo was lean and hungry after his long winter's sleep. He went hunting for insects in the newly spaded garden.

All summer Bufo hunted in the garden. His hunting helped the garden, for Bufo ate many insects and other pests that he found on the vegetables. Sometimes he ate hundreds of them at a meal!

Bufo's tongue was attached at the front of his mouth, not at the back like the tongues of most animals. Because of this, he could throw it out and catch food several inches away. Insects stuck to the sticky tongue and were pulled right into his mouth!

Bufo was not particular about what he ate. He ate moths. He gulped down beetles that he found on the bean plants. He swallowed little woolly caterpillars, fuzzy hairs and all. He snapped up fireflies that glowed as they went down.

Garden slugs, sow bugs, crickets, earthworms—all went into Bufo's stomach. He ate his fill every night—thousands of insects a month.

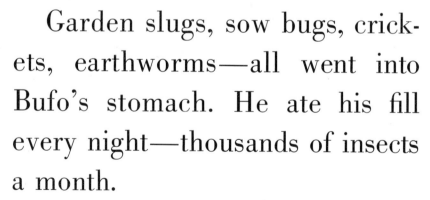

One evening Bufo swallowed a
bee. He gulped several times and
blinked in surprise. Maybe he
didn't like that so much!

Every night after he had finished his hunting, Bufo went back to his hole under the rock in the springhouse. He always backed into his burrow. Here he rested all through the heat of the day. When evening shadows began to creep across the lawn, Bufo woke up and went out hunting again.

A wandering skunk almost got him one night. But Bufo wriggled through the fence and got away.

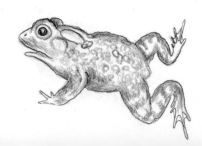

Another night a hungry screech owl pounced down at him. Bufo hopped under a big rock just in time.

Year after year, Bufo lived in his hole beside the spring. He ate insects and grew bigger, and fatter than ever. It would be three or four years, however, before he was big enough to go back to the pond to breed. Toads can live for many years.

Sometimes his skin became tight like a suit that is too small. Then it split down the back and underneath. Bufo wriggled and squirmed and worked his way out of the old skin. Then he ate it! The new skin underneath was bigger and looser. But Bufo would grow into it.

A toad's skin is rough and warty, and some people think that anyone who handles a toad will get warts too. That is not so.

In the autumn of his third year Bufo was fat and saucy. He was nearly four inches long and almost as wide when he dug himself into his hole for the winter.

The next spring he was as hungry as usual after his winter's sleep. When he hopped out from under the springhouse rock, a honeybee was buzzing around a violet nearby. But Bufo blinked and turned away. Honeybees could be disagreeable to eat.

The farmyard was full of noise. The big red rooster flapped his wings and crowed loudly. The calves bawled for their evening milk. The horses neighed at the watering trough. But Bufo heard only one sound. What was it?

It was a high trilling sound coming from the pond in the pasture—first one voice, then many. It was a chorus of toads.

Bufo blinked and gaped. Then he started off through the green yard. He would go to the pond too. He was a big toad now.

Past the garden he hopped, past the pigpen, on through the rocky barnyard. Finally he scrambled under the fence into the low meadow. Soon he would be at the pond.

Suddenly the farmer's dog dashed up. He grabbed Bufo in his mouth. Bufo just closed his eyes and played dead. A very disagreeable-tasting fluid oozed out of the glands in his skin. When the dog tasted it, he wrinkled up his nose in disgust and dropped Bufo. He would go hunting for rabbits. Rabbits were harder to catch, but they tasted better.

Bufo opened his eyes. He gulped. Then on he hopped toward the pond.

It was springtime, time for Bufo to be in the pond with the other toads. He would trill too. Hop—hop—hop!